SO-AFY-289

PRACTICE AND ACTIVITY WORKBOOK

The *McGraw-Hill* Companies

Macmillan
McGraw-Hill

Published by Macmillan/McGraw-Hill, of McGraw-Hill Education, a division of The McGraw-Hill Companies, Inc.,
Two Penn Plaza, New York, New York 10121.

Printed in the United States of America

9 MAL 13 12

© Macmillan/McGraw-Hill

Contents

Supporting the Main Idea

Read the paragraph below. Then fill in the chart by listing the main idea and supporting details from the paragraph. For help with this skill, see pages 52–53 in your textbook.

Scientists have differing theories about how the first settlers came to the Americas. Most scientists believe that, during the last Ice Age, people from Asia walked across the land bridge we call Beringia into what is now Alaska. They were hunting animals for food. However, some scientists believe the first settlers made the trip by boat. They may have sailed south along the Pacific coast from Asia or east from Europe along the edge of the glaciers. Other scientists theorize that people came by raft from Australia.

Main Idea and Details Chart

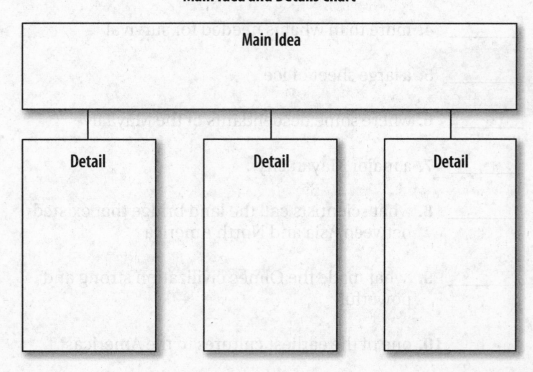

Name _____ Date _____

America's First Settlers

Match each term in the box with its meaning by writing the correct answer on the line. For help, see pages 58–61 in your textbook.

a. Beringia	**e.** trade	**i.** Tikal
b. Ice Age	**f.** surplus	**j.** Guatemala
c. Olmec	**g.** Three Sisters	**k.** glacier
d. Maya	**h.** archaeologist	

_____ **1.** a person who studies artifacts from the past

_____ **2.** a group that traded with the Olmec

_____ **3.** a period of unusual coldness on Earth

_____ **4.** more than what is needed for survival

_____ **5.** a large sheet of ice

_____ **6.** where some descendants of the Maya live

_____ **7.** a major Mayan city

_____ **8.** what scientists call the land bridge that existed between Asia and North America

_____ **9.** what made the Olmec civilization strong and powerful

_____ **10.** one of the earliest cultures in the Americas

_____ **11.** crops of corn, beans, and squash

Standards: 5.1.1, 5.1.2, 5.1.3   Chapter 1, Lesson 1

Tracking Two Peoples

Use the parallel time line below to answer the questions that follow.
For help, see pages 60–61 in your textbook.

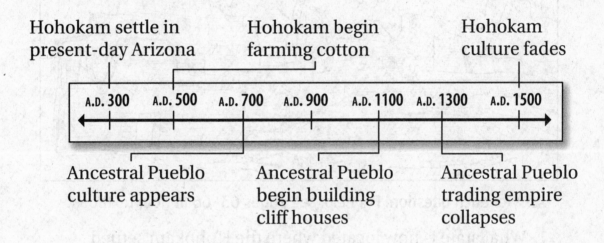

Hohokam settle in present-day Arizona

Hohokam begin farming cotton

Hohokam culture fades

A.D. 300   A.D. 500   A.D. 700   A.D. 900   A.D. 1100   A.D. 1300   A.D. 1500

Ancestral Pueblo culture appears

Ancestral Pueblo begin building cliff houses

Ancestral Pueblo trading empire collapses

1. What two cultures are compared on this parallel time line?

   _____

2. What is the time span of the time line?

   _____

   Into what segments is the time line divided?

   _____

3. Which culture existed longer? _____

4. How many years after the Hohokam began farming cotton did the Ancestral Pueblo begin building cliff houses?

   _____

Remembering the Hohokam and Pueblo Peoples

Answer each question. For help, see pages 63–66 in your textbook.

1. What state is now located where the Hohokam settled around 300 A.D.? _____

2. What made this choice of location unusual?

_____

3. What were some activities at which the Hohokam were skilled?

_____

_____

4. Using present-day geography, where did the Ancestral Pueblo, or Anasazi, live?

_____

_____

5. What purposes did Chaco Canyon serve? What was it like?

_____

_____

_____

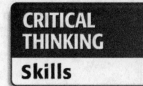

Find the Solution

Fill out the table below. For each problem, write the solution found by the Hohokam or the Ancestral Pueblo. For help with this skill, see page 67 in your textbook.

Problem	Solution
The Hohokam lived in a desert where little rain fell, but they still needed to grow crops.	
Different crops needed to be watered by the Hohokam at different times and in different amounts.	
The land the Ancestral Pueblo lived on could not be irrigated in the same way as the Hohokam land.	
The Ancestral Pueblo needed to protect themselves against enemies.	

The Mound Builders

Answer each question using one or more complete sentences. For help, see pages 69-71 in your textbook.

1. What do we call the three mound building cultures?

_____

_____

2. Why do we give the Adena and Mississippian these names?

_____

_____

_____

3. The mounds were used for what purposes?

_____

_____

_____

4. Apart from mound building, what did the three mound building cultures have in common?

_____

_____

_____

_____

Native Americans of the West

Look at the picture and answer the following questions. For help, see pages 78-85 in your textbook.

1. The picture shows how daily life among the Tlingit might have looked long ago. What can you tell from looking at the picture about how and where they lived?

_____

_____

_____

_____

2. What is one feature of traditional Tlingit culture you know about that is NOT shown in the picture?

_____

_____

_____

Name _____ Date _____

People of the Southwest

Complete the crossword puzzle. For help, see pages 85–92 in your textbook.

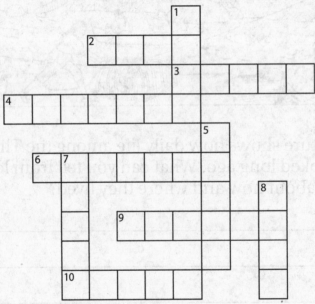

Clues

Across

2. what the Navajo call themselves
3. an important animal to the Navajo
4. doll important in Hopi religion and education
6. potter who renewed interest in traditional Hopi pottery
9. with *Old*, one of the oldest settlements in the U.S.
10. what the name *Apache* means

Down

1. a mountain with a flat top
5. dome-shaped Navajo home
7. home-building material of the Pueblo and Hopi
8. special room for religious ceremonies

Standards: 5.1.1, 5.1.2, 5.1.3   Chapter 2, Lesson 2

People of the Plains

Help David complete his essay about the American Indians of the Plains, by filling in the missing information below. For help, see pages 95–101 in your textbook.

People of the Plains
By David Black

Groups of American Indians, including the _____ _____ lived in the Great Plains region of North America. This region has a climate that is _____. The most important resource for the American Indians living on the plains was the _____, which was used for _____. Two types of houses made by the Plains people were _____.

Horses arrived in the Great Plains in _____. Horses changed the Plains peoples' lives by _____ _____ _____.

The Plains people valued traits such as _____ _____ _____.

Children learned skills by _____ _____ _____ _____.

Name _____ Date _____

People of the Eastern Woodland

Draw lines connecting each American Indian tribe to the activities someone in that tribe might have done. Draw a dotted line from the Creek to its activities, a solid line from the Cherokee to its activities, and a squiggly line from the Iroquois to its activities. For help, see pages 103–110 in your textbook.

If you were a

1. Creek

2. Cherokee

3. Iroquois

You might

a. make wampum

b. speak Muskogean

c. plant the Three Sisters

d. celebrate the Green Corn Festival

e. hunt animals

f. speak Iroquoian

g. live in a longhouse

h. make clothing and blankets

Standards: 5.1.1, 5.1.2, 5.1.3 Chapter 2, Lesson 4

Native Americans and Their Environments

Think about the many Native American peoples you learned about in this unit. They lived in different environments. Naturally, their environments influenced the kinds of houses they lived in, the types of food they ate, how they thought about the world around them, and even what they did for fun.

1. With a partner, choose a Native American group that you have learned about in Chapter 1 or 2.

2. Create a poster showing members of your chosen group in their natural environment. The poster should show how the environment in which the Native American group lived influenced their way of life.

3. Put the name of your group on the top of the poster.

4. Draw pictures of the arts, housing, tools, and other items you think were important to their culture.

5. Present your poster to the class. You should explain how you believe the environment influenced your group, pointing out the details shown in your poster.

Name _____ Date _____

Putting Events in Order

Fill in the chart by listing the events from the paragraph below in the correct sequence. For help with this skill, see pages 124–125 in your textbook.

In 1488 a captain from Lisbon, Bartolomeu Dias, managed to sail around the southern tip of Africa. Nearing southern Africa, Dias's two caravels were hit by a terrible storm. Their navigational tools were useless because they could not see the horizon.

When the storm died down, Dias realized that his ships were heading north, and land was on their left. They had rounded Africa's Cape of Good Hope and reached the Indian Ocean. Dias returned to Portugal and described his adventures to the king.

Sequence of Events Chart

First Event

↓

Second Event

↓

Third Event

© Macmillan/McGraw-Hill

Name _____ Date _____

Europe Faces Change

Write the correct word next to its definition below. Then find the hidden word in the puzzle. Words may be written up, down, forward or backward. For help, see pages 129–133 in your textbook.

```
A R G U T E N B E R G S G N I K I V
S I U T E R O P X E A I U Y N W Z A
C O U N T E R R E F O R M A T I O N
H S Y A V C I G W O B T A W E R P I
O H T T A O K J P R M N R C V O A C
P O I S U N Y T R M E R C H A N T L
A S D E I Q N V C A X Z O L D F T Y
K I N T Y U B T V T R C P E X Q Z O
M I B O I I C T Y I O M O O R S T E
J V C R U S A D E O U V L P M W S D
P R W P H T K L I N B C O V B E D R
    M A R T I N L U T H E R I F
```

1. Catholic Church's response to the Reformation

   _____

2. war waged by Christians for control of holy places

   _____

3. first European known to visit China _____

4. a person who buys and sell goods _____

5. Roman Catholic priest who began the Reformation

   _____

6. bookseller who invented a new type of printing

   _____

7. Muslims of Arab origin

   _____

8. follower of Martin Luther

   _____

9. the movement Martin Luther began _____

10. Norse traders and raiders who traveled by sea _____

11. name for recapture of Spain by Christians _____

Asian and African Trade

For each question, circle the correct answer. For help, see pages 136–138 in your textbook.

1. Europeans traded along the Silk Road for. . .

   a. gold.   b. spices.   c. ships.

2. Zheng He . . .

   a. led a trading expedition.

   b. sailed to the Americas.

   c. commanded a small ship and sailing crew.

3. The compass was . . .

   a. used first by Chinese sailors.

   b. used first by Arab traders.

   c. something Marco Polo brought back from China.

4. The Arabs who traded in West Africa . . .

   a. brought much gold with them.

   b. influenced people's religion.

   c. built the Songhai empire.

5. A journey on the Silk Road was expensive because . . .

   a. the route was secret and only available for a fee.

   b. most of the trade goods would spoil on the way back.

   c. it took a long time and required paying for ships and camels.

Using Latitude and Longitude

Use the world map below to answer the questions. For help with
this skill, see pages 140-141 in your textbook.

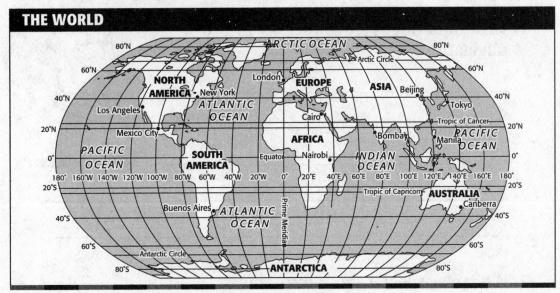

1. What feature is at 0° of latitude? _____

2. Through which continents does 0° of longitude run?

   _____

3. If you were at 40°N and 80°E, what continent would you
   be in? _____

4. Between which latitudes is Antarctica located?

   _____

5. The Tropic of Cancer is at 23 1/3°N latitude, and the
   Tropic of Capricorn is at 23 1/3°S latitude. They are the
   northern and southern edges of what we call the tropics.
   Which continents are largely in the tropics?

   _____

6. Name the approximate line of latitude and longitude for
   your own location. _____

   _____

Name _____ Date _____

New Routes to Riches

Answer each question below. For help, see pages 142–145 in your textbook.

Prince Henry

1. How did Prince Henry's school improve navigation?

_____

_____

_____

_____

_____

2. What was special about the caravel?

_____

_____

_____

_____

3. How did Portuguese explorations affect the people of Africa and India?

_____

_____

_____

_____

A New World

Look carefully at the routes Columbus traveled on his first and
third voyages. Then answer the questions below. For help, see
pages 150–155 in your textbook.

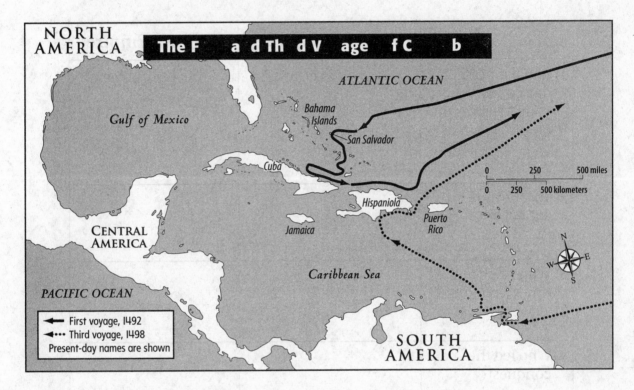

1. Columbus visited one small island and two large ones
   on his first voyage. What are their present-day names?

   _____

2. On his third voyage, Columbus reached the coast of
   South America and then sailed north, revisiting which
   two Caribbean islands? _____

3. What foods were introduced into Europe as a result of
   the Columbian exchange? _____

   _____

   _____

Name _____ Date _____

Two Lost Empires

Complete the chart with information about how the Inca and the Aztec empires were conquered by the Spaniards. For help, see pages 156–161 in your textbook.

	The Aztec Empire	The Inca Empire
1. In what present-day country or countries was the empire located?		
2. What was the capital city?		
3. Who ruled at the time of conquest?		
4. Who led the conquest?		
5. What special factors helped the conquerors succeed?		
6. What did the conquerors want?		

© Macmillan/McGraw-Hill

Standards: 5.2.1, 5.2.2, 5.2.4, 5.3.2, 5.3.4   Chapter 4, Lesson 2

Name _____ Date _____

This Is Your Life

Look at the three pictures showing life in New Spain. Read the
sentences below them. Draw a line from each sentence to the picture it
matches. For help, see pages 166–171 in your textbook.

Peninsulares held high government and church jobs.	Enslaved Africans were brought to replace Native American laborers.	Native Americans received little or no money for their work.

Choose a person in one of the pictures. Write a few more
sentences about him or her.

_____

_____

_____

_____

_____

Exploring America

Use the map to answer the questions. For help, see pages 174–181 in your textbook.

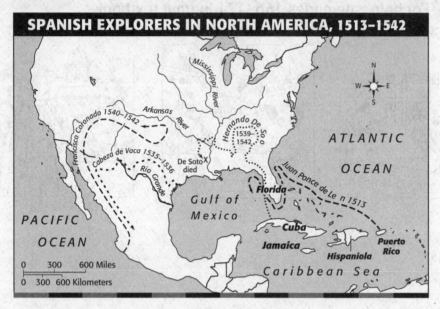

SPANISH EXPLORERS IN NORTH AMERICA, 1513–1542

1. Which explorer made the earliest expedition? _____
   _____ Where did he explore? _____

2. Which explorer started out in what is now Mexico?
   _____

3. Which explorer completed his expedition in Mexico?
   _____

4. Whose expedition lasted the longest? _____
   During which years did he explore? _____

5. What feature on the map indicates where de Soto died?
   _____

6. Which two explorers crossed the same river? _____
   _____ Which river was it? _____

7. Which major rivers did de Soto cross? _____
   _____

Name _____ Date _____

The Northwest Passage

Read each clue. Write each word in the blank spaces. Use the letters already provided. For help, see pages 187–190 in your textbook.

2   5   10   11   16
___ ___   ___ ___   ___
  3   4   7   8   13
  ___ ___   ___ ___   ___   ___
1   6   9   ___
___   ___   ___   12   14
                                         ___   ___
| N | O | R | T | H | W | E | S | T | | P | A | S | S | A | ¹⁵G | E |

___   ___   ___   ___   ___

___   ___   ___   ___   ___

___   ___   ___   ___

                                                       ___

1. The country where Hudson Bay is located
2. Cabot, Verrazano, and Hudson
3. What the Northwest Passage was thought to be
4. The ocean where the Northwest Passage really is
5. A person who trades goods for profit
6. The state where the Hudson River is found today
7. How many miles wide Henry Hudson thought North America was
8. An English explorer hired by the Dutch
9. The name for people from the Netherlands
10. Friendly Native Americans in New York
11. The Italian explorer who found New York harbor
12. The continent the explorers were trying to reach
13. The great resource of the Grand Banks
14. Explorer hired by the King of England
15. Cabot's important discovery
16. The country that set up the first merchant company

Name _____ Date _____

Is It Fact or Opinion?

Read each statement and mark it F for fact or O for opinion. Then, for each one you marked as a fact, write whether or not you can check to see if it is true. For each one you marked as an opinion, briefly explain how you know it is an opinion. For help, see page 191 in your textbook.

_____ **1.** Many rulers and merchants wanted to find the Northwest Passage.

_____

_____ **2.** Finding the Northwest Passage was worth any amount of money a king or company had to spend.

_____

_____ **3.** The first merchant company was founded in the Netherlands in 1602.

_____

_____ **4.** The Lenape were friendly people.

_____

_____ **5.** Henry Hudson got closer to the real Northwest Passage on his second expedition.

_____

_____ **6.** The Dutch merchant company that hired Henry Hudson made a wise choice.

_____

Standards: 5.2.1, 5.2.2, 5.2.4   Chapter 5, Identify Fact and Opinion

New France

Answer each question. For help, see pages 192–197 in your textbook.

1. Name at least three men who helped explore and claim land for New France.

   _____

   _____

2. What bodies of water did French explorers hope would turn out to be the Northwest Passage?

   _____

3. The French hoped to find wealth in the New World. Describe their experience.

   _____

   _____

4. Name two similarities between French and Spanish interests in the New World.

   _____

   _____

   _____

5. Name two differences between the French and Spanish experiences in the New World.

   _____

   _____

   _____

Name _____ Date _____

Change in the Americas

Complete each sentence below using one item from each box. Then order the events by numbering 1-7 in the circles. For help, see pages 198-203 in your textbook.

The Lost Colony	1585
John Smith	1587 and 1590
John Rolfe	1606
royal governor	1609–1610
Roanoke Island	1614
King James I	1619
House of Burgesses	1624

◯ 1. _____ granted a charter to a group of merchants called the Virginia Company in _____.

◯ 2. Virginia's elected government, the _____, first met in _____, the same year a Dutch ship brought the first African captives to Jamestown.

◯ 3. The Jamestown colonists missed the leadership of _____ during the Starving Time, from _____.

◯ 4. The first English colonists in America settled at _____ in _____.

◯ 5. The Virginia Company lost control of Jamestown when the king appointed a _____ in _____.

◯ 6. The second settlement at Roanoke is called _____ because the people mysteriously vanished sometime between _____.

◯ 7. In _____ the first successful tobacco crop was harvested by _____.

When Worlds Collide

What happens when very different cultures meet for the first time? During the time of exploration of the Americas, these meetings happened all the time. How did people communicate without knowing each other's language?

1. With your teacher's help, form six small groups. Three groups will be made up of Native Americans. The other three will be Europeans. Each group of Native Americans should pair off with a group of Europeans and begin communicating.

2. With your combined group, create a news broadcast to show how the Europeans and the Native Americans interacted with each other. Everyone in your group should have a role in the broadcast.

3. Present your "meetings" to the rest of the class.

Name _____ Date _____

Sum It Up

Read the two paragraphs below. Then fill in the chart by summarizing the information in them. For help with this skill, see pages 216–217 in your textbook.

Oglethorpe knew that if he wanted his new colony to succeed, he would need to make friends with the Native Americans in the area. The most powerful group among them was the Creek Confederacy. Several independent Creek villages had formed the confederacy to protect their lands.

Another Creek group, the Yamacraw, lived in the area. They were not part of the confederacy. However, they lived near Yamacraw Bluff, where Oglethorpe wanted to build his settlement. Oglethorpe became friends with Tomochichi, the leader of the Yamacraw. Chief Tomochichi agreed to sell Oglethorpe Yamacraw Bluff for his new settlement, Savannah.

Summary Chart

Paragraph 1	Paragraph 2

Standards: 5.3.1, 5.3.2, 5.4.1, 5.4.2   Unit 3, Summarize

© Macmillan/McGraw-Hill

New Colonies, New Lives

Look at the map. Then answer each question by writing the place name on the correct line. For help, see pages 220-225 in your textbook.

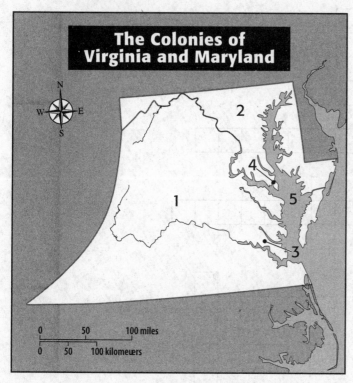

1. _____

2. _____

3. _____

4. _____

5. _____

1. Which colony grew west and north of the James River?

2. Which colony did Lord Baltimore found?

3. What city became the capital of Virginia in 1699?

4. What did Lord Baltimore name the village he bought from the Yoacomoco?

5. What bay had a harbor deep enough for large ships?

Name _____ Date _____

Southern Colonies Crossword

Use the clues below to fill in the crossword puzzle. For help, see pages 228–232 in your textbook.

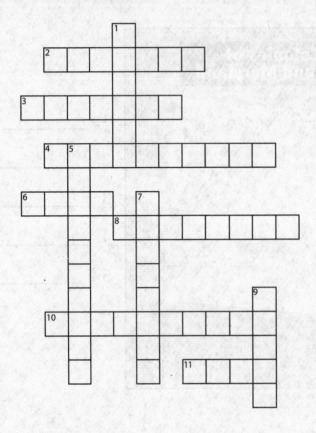

Across

2. Europeans with a colony to the south of Georgia
3. The name of the "colony to the south" referred to in Clue 2 Across
4. Native American chief who became Oglethorpe's friend
6. A product that was unsuccessful in Georgia
8. Georgia's first English settlement
10. Someone who owns land or a business

11. This crop was tended by enslaved Africans bought by wealthy Carolina colonists

Down

1. A valuable crop used to make blue dye
5. The founder of the Georgia colony
7. Native American group that sold land for the Georgia settlement
9. Confederacy of Native Americans living in Georgia

Standards: 5.3.2, 5.4.1, 5.4.2, 5.4.3   Chapter 6, Lesson 2

Creating an Outline

Read about life for African Americans in the Southern colonies on pages 236–237 in your textbook. Then complete the outline below. Remember to include only the most important facts. For help with this skill, see page 233 in your textbook.

African American families

  I. Slavery on plantations

    A. People lived in small, poorly made cabins.

    B. Work started at sunup and ended at sundown.

    C. _____

    _____

    D. _____

    _____

  II. Blending ways of life

    A. Africans combined their traditions with new ways of life.

    B. _____

    C. _____

  III. Churches

    A. _____

    _____

    B. _____

    _____

    C. _____

  IV. Free African Americans

    A. _____

    _____

    B. _____

    _____

    C. _____

    _____

Name _____ Date _____

What Would It Be Like?

Describe the work and responsibilities of each group of people listed in the chart. For help, see pages 236-241 in your textbook.

People	Work and Responsibilities
Free African Americans living in the country	
Owners of small farms, former European indentured servants	
Children of farm owners living near a small community, not wealthy	
Owners of large plantations in North Carolina	
Native Americans in backcountry, early 1700s	
Enslaved Africans on a large plantation, 1750	

Standards: 5.3.2, 5.3.3, 5.4.6   Chapter 6, Lesson 3

Pilgrim Puzzle

Fill in the blanks with the answer for each clue. Then use the
letters in the box to answer the riddle at the bottom of the page.
For help, see pages 246–251 in your textbook.

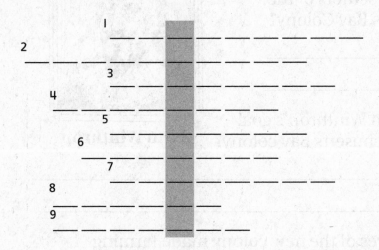

1. a Native American group that befriended the Pilgrims

2. people who wanted to set up their own churches

3. the name of the Pilgrims' first settlement

4. the second governor of the Pilgrims' settlement

5. Samoset's greeting to the Pilgrims: "_____
Englishmen!"

6. a sachem who helped the Pilgrims

7. the Native American group that Squanto belonged to

8. the Wampanoag word for "leader"

9. person who travels for religious purposes

Riddle

What was the Pilgrims' favorite flower? The _____

A Puritan Portrait

Answer the questions. For help, see pages 254-257 in your textbook.

1. Why was this man important to the Puritan settlers of the Massachusetts Bay Colony?

   _____

   _____

John Winthrop

2. What was John Winthrop's goal for the Massachusetts Bay colony?

   _____

   _____

3. **a.** What features of the new colony made farming difficult?

   _____

   b. What features helped the colony grow?

   _____

   _____

4. What was the role of Puritan men in governing the colony?

   _____

   _____

   _____

5. What was the purpose of Puritan education?

   _____

   _____

   _____

Standards: 5.4.1, 5.4.2, 5.4.3, 5.4.7   Chapter 7, Lesson 2

Looking at a Cutaway Diagram

Analyze this cutaway diagram of the *Mayflower*. Then answer the questions. For help with this skill, see pages 256–257 in your textbook.

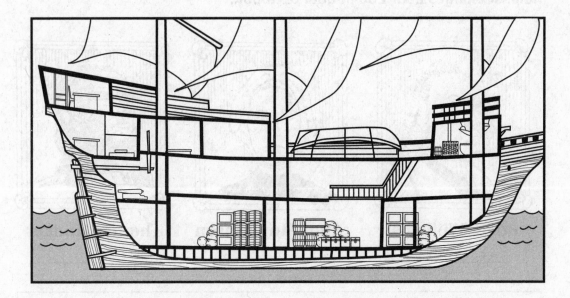

1. About what fraction of the boat, apart from masts and sails, is below the surface of the water?

   _____

2. What can you learn about the *Mayflower* from a cutaway diagram that you could not learn from a regular drawing? _____

   _____

3. Why do you think the heaviest items are stored in the bottom of the ship? _____

   _____

4. What other structures mentioned in this chapter could be shown using a cutaway diagram?

   _____

   _____

Conflicts and Colonies

Read the statements below and place the letter of the statement under the correct portrait. Then answer the questions that follow. For help, see pages 258–260 in your textbook.

Roger Williams
_____

Anne Hutchinson
_____

Thomas Hooker
_____

Statements of Belief

A. People can interpret the Bible for themselves.

B. All men, not just Puritans, should be allowed to vote.

C. Colonies should tolerate different religious beliefs. They should not take Native American lands.

1. Roger Williams, Anne Hutchinson, and Thomas Hooker were considered Puritan rebels. Why?

_____

_____

2. When Anne Hutchinson stood by her beliefs, Puritan leaders forced her to leave Massachusetts. What did she do after that?

_____

_____

The Puritan Way

Read the questions. Then circle the letter next to the correct answer.
For help, see pages 262–265 in your textbook.

1. Most Puritans worked as
   a. teachers
   b. farmers
   c. blacksmiths

2. Younger Puritan children weeded gardens, helped around the house, and
   a. cooked
   b. plucked feathers from geese
   c. cleaned the barn

3. Puritans used hornbooks because
   a. they liked horns
   b. paper was expensive
   c. they didn't know how to read

4. Puritans believed that it was more important to teach girls to take care of households than to
   a. make butter
   b. read, write, and do math
   c. dye cloth

5. At age 8, a Puritan boy could attend grammar school, stay home and work with his father, or become
   a. an apprentice
   b. a teacher
   c. a journeyman

6. In 1636, the Puritans started a college in Massachusetts. They called the school Harvard because
   a. it was in a town called Harvard
   b. Harvard was a respected school in Great Britain
   c. John Harvard gave the school books and money for a library

Name _____ Date _____

New York and New Jersey News

Read each headline and answer the questions. For help,
see pages 274–277 in your textbook.

1. a. In what year would this headline have
appeared? _____

b. From whom did the Dutch purchase
Manhattan Island?

_____

Dutch Buy Island

Rename island New
Amsterdam

2. a. In what year would this headline have
appeared? _____

b. Who was the leader of the Dutch
colony at this time?

_____

**New Netherland
Surrenders to English**

Today an English fleet
arrived in New Amsterdam
harbor.

3. a. What encouraged a diverse population
to settle in New York and New Jersey?

_____

_____

b. Whaling was very dangerous yet the
industry continued to grow. Why?

_____

_____

**Whale of a Tale
As Colonies Grow**

Officials note that colonies
continue to attract a
diverse population.

© Macmillan/McGraw-Hill

Geography Skills

Look at the picture and quote below. Then answer the questions that follow. For help, see pages 278–283 in your textbook.

I am very sensible of unkindness and injustice that hath been too much exercised toward you by the people of these parts of the world, but I am not such a man.

—*William Penn*

1. Why did William Penn want to start his own colony?

_____

_____

2. Why did King Charles II give Penn the land for a colony?

_____

_____

_____

_____

3. What event in William Penn's life does the picture show?

_____

_____

4. How did the relationship between the Lenape and the European settlers change after William Penn's death?

_____

_____

_____

Name _____ Date _____

Lies About Life in the Middle Colonies

Each of the following statements is false. Draw a line through the false part, and write a true statement below. For help, see pages 284-288 in your textbook.

1. The economy of the Middle Colonies was based on mining and trade.

_____

_____

2. Colonists taught Native Americans how to gather maple syrup and remove trees by "girdling."

_____

_____

3. The tradition of tolerance and justice applied to all who lived in the Middle Colonies.

_____

_____

4. In the 1700s, immigrants like Gottlieb Mittelberger came to America to escape the plague in Europe.

_____

_____

_____

Standards: 5.4.3, 5.4.5 Chapter 8, Lesson 3

Colonies Cause Conflict

Look at the names of the people and groups in the box below. Then, write each name associated with a conflict in the box for either New England or the Southern colonies. For help, see pages 292–297 in your textbook.

Yamasee	**Wampanoag**	**Tuscarora**
Massasoit	**John Lawson**	**Metacomet**
Pequot	**Narragansett**	**Opechancanough**

New England

People	Groups
_____	_____
_____	_____
_____	_____

Southern Colonies

People	Groups
_____	_____
_____	_____
_____	_____

The Geography of Slavery

Read each statement. Circle either true or false. For each false statement, write the true fact. For help, see pages 299–303 in your textbook.

1. Slavery was never legal in the U.S. colonies.

TRUE   FALSE

_____

_____

2. Slave traders kidnapped thousands of Africans to work as unpaid slaves.

TRUE   FALSE

_____

3. Most Africans survived the journey from Africa to America.

TRUE   FALSE

_____

_____

_____

4. Enslaved Africans often wrote stories to teach their children about their lives.

TRUE   FALSE

_____

_____

5. The slave codes were laws that gave slaves more freedom.

TRUE   FALSE

_____

_____

_____

_____

Making Money in the Colonies

Use the terms in the box to complete the passage. For help, see pages 306–311 in your textbook.

taxes	manufactured goods	surplus
Middle Passage	tyranny	triangular trade
free enterprise	smuggling	industry
cash crops	shipbuilding	

In New England, _____ became a very successful _____. In the Middle Colonies, farmers often had a _____ of crops that they could sell. In New England and the Middle Colonies, _____ were also produced. Southern Colonies raised money from _____ such as tobacco and indigo.

The English rulers wanted to limit colonists' _____, or control of their own businesses, in order to protect and help the English economy. They added _____ to prices to make colonial products more expensive and less appealing to other nations. To avoid the trade laws, colonists began hiding or _____ products.

The colonists competed with England along three-sided trade routes known as the _____. The _____ was the section of the voyage that went between Africa and the West Indies. Over time, the colonists saw English attempts to control trade as a form of _____. It would lead to serious problems in the coming years.

Who Does What?

Draw an arrow from each phrase to the picture of the colonial government or position it describes. For help, see pages 312–317 in your textbook.

1. Chosen by the king of England or the owner of a colony

2. Represented citizens of a town or county

3. Created by each colony's charter

4. Officials elected at town meetings

5. Controlled colony's money

6. Represented interests of the king

7. Had power to reject laws passed by the assembly

8. Used Parliament as a model

9. Allowed male voters to speak and vote at meetings

Royal Governor

Colonial Assembly

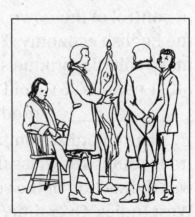

Local Government

© Macmillan/McGraw-Hill

Difficult Decisions

Read this passage on the experiences of enslaved African Americans in the colonies. Then answer the questions about the difficult decisions these people had to make. For help with this skill, see page 318 in your textbook.

Enslaved African Americans looked for ways to fight back against the colonists. Enslaved workers resisted their situation by slowing their work or by breaking or losing tools. Others ran away. Some hoped to find freedom in less settled areas. Others hoped to find family members who had been sold away.

On occasion, enslaved Africans rebelled violently. Although armed rebellion was rare, it was a constant fear among European colonists. Twice within 30 years, serious slave rebellions rocked the English colonies.

The first slave revolt was in New York City in 1712. A slave named Coffee led about 25 Africans and two Native Americans in a surprise attack. They set fire to a building and waited for a crowd to gather. Then they opened fire and killed several colonists.

There was a severe reaction to this revolt. Almost all of the rebels were quickly captured and killed. European colonists wanted to frighten enslaved Africans into accepting their enslavement.

1. List three ways that enslaved people might fight back against slavery. _____

_____

2. What do you think were the likely results of each of these alternatives? _____

_____

_____

_____

3. Why do you think the alternatives presented these people with such a difficult decision to make? _____

_____

_____

_____

Following a Dream

Think about the many reasons people settled new lands in the English colonies. Which person's or group of people's reasons for settling in the colonies are most interesting to you?

1. Working with a partner or small group, learn what you can about the person or group you chose: their lives before they came to the colonies; what they hoped to achieve by settling in the new lands; and how they felt about their new lives. (Go online or use the library for more information about them.)

2. Brainstorm with your group to create characters for a short play about the period.

3. Create one or more characters for each member of your group to play. You can use the chart below to help your group get started. A few ideas for one possible character have been filled in for you. Add a row in the chart for each character you create.

4. Write dialogue for your characters to speak in a short play with two scenes: "Before We Left England" and "After We Arrived in the Colony."

5. After writing your play and revising it, choose sets and costumes.

6. Rehearse your play before performing it for the class.

Characters	Reason(s) for Going to the Colony	Life in the Old Country	Life in the New Colony	Feelings About His or Her New Life
Anne, 25 years old	wanted the freedom to practice her religion	comfortable; had servants to help with the housework and care for her children	life of hardships; does all housework, herself; is afraid of not having enough food to feed her children	glad to have the freedom to practice her religion; wishes life was not so hard for her and her children now

© Macmillan/McGraw-Hill

Standards: 5.4.1, 5.4.2, 5.4.3, 5.4.5, 5.4.6   Unit 3, Unit Activity

What Happened As a Result?

Read the paragraphs below. Then fill in the chart by listing causes and effects from the paragraphs. We have filled in the first cause for you. For help with this skill, see pages 332–333 in your textbook.

In response to Spain's fear that Russia or England would settle California, Gálvez had come up with a plan. He wanted Spain to send soldiers to build forts in California as well as Catholic missionaries to convert the Native Americans there to Christianity.

In 1768 Gálvez traveled to San Blas on the Pacific Coast of present-day Mexico to order ships for the expedition. He chose Father Junípero Serra to head the new missions. Even though this Franciscan priest had a painful injured leg, he was a tireless worker.

Cause and Effect Chart

Cause		Effect
1. Spain feared that Russia or England would settle California.		1.
2.		2.

Name _____ Date _____

Settlements A-Cross California

Use the clues to complete the puzzle. For help, see pages 338–343 in your textbook.

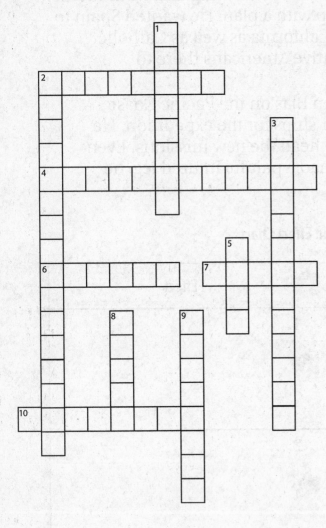

Across

2. location of first mission in Alta California

4. Spanish for "The Royal Road"

6. a Spanish farming village

7. chosen by Gálvez to head new missions

10. mission founded by Serra in 1770

Down

1. Spanish word for fort

2. expedition ordered by Gálvez to enlarge the Spanish empire and convert Native Americans in California

3. nickname for a Spanish soldier

5. governor who offered incentives for farmers to settle in California

8. mud bricks used for building

9. Native Americans who lived in the area of what is now San Diego

Standards: 5.2.2, 5.3.1, 5.3.2, 5.3.4   Chapter 10, Lesson 1

Forts, Furs, and the French

Complete each sentence with the correct word or date from the box. Then number the sentences to show the correct order of events. For help, see pages 344–349 in your textbook.

Chicago	**Detroit**	**fort**
Montreal	**Michigan**	**1682**
New Orleans	**Louisiana**	**1779**
Erie	**tributaries**	

____ Bienville founded the city of _____ in 1718.

____ In _____, du Sable founded a trading post on Lake _____ that would later become _____.

____ Louis XIV sent d'Iberville to establish settlements in _____.

____ La Salle claimed the Mississippi River and its _____ for France in _____.

____ Antoine De La Mothe started out from _____ with soldiers, colonists, and missionaries. When he reached the end of Lake _____ he founded a _____ called Pontchartrain du _____.

What was the importance of the fur trade to New France?

_____

_____

CRITICAL THINKING Skills

Name ______________________ Date ____________

Identifying Stereotypes

Read the paragraph and look for stereotypes. List the stereotypes in the first column of the chart below. In the second column, write how you know it is a stereotype. For help with this skill, see pages 348–349 in your textbook.

The Europeans who settled in the North American continent did so for a variety of reasons. The Spanish were only interested in gold. The French only hoped to get rich from the fur trade. Everyone who came from England wanted religious freedom. None of the European colonists cared about the well-being of the Native Americans.

Stereotype	How I Know

Conflict Creates Change

Complete the newspaper article by filling in the blanks.
For help, see pages 350-355 in your textbook.

WAR ENDS!
British claim victory!

The long and bloody conflict known as the _____ came to an end when both France and Great Britain signed the _____. The treaty gives Britain control of French lands east of the _____ River. Much of the credit for the British victory goes to _____, a leader who poured money, troops, and equipment into the war. Until that point, the _____ seemed to be winning the war. Much of France's early success was possible because of help from their Native American friends, the _____. Although the defeat means the French can no longer help _____, Great Britain seems to have helped their cause by issuing the _____. This official statement sets aside all British land west of the _____ for Native Americans. The purpose of the proclamation was to _____. It has calmed many Native Americans, but angered many _____. They are upset because the new proclamation prevents them from _____. Many colonists plan to move west, anyway. Their anger unites them against Great Britian.

Name _____ Date _____

Colonies Unite in Protest

Study the political cartoon. Then answer the following questions. For help, see pages 360-364 in your textbook.

"Take back your trash"

1. Who do the people on the left of the cartoon represent?

_____

2. Why were the colonists angry over the Intolerable Acts, the Townshend Acts, and the Stamp Act? _____

_____

_____

_____

3. Describe two other decisions by the British government and tell why they angered colonists. _____

_____

_____

_____

_____

4. The cartoon shows the colonists "throwing back" the acts. In reality, how did they react to the Stamp Act and the Townshend Act? What was the result? _____

_____

Who? What? Where? When?

Use the names of people and places in the box to complete the sentences below. For help, see pages 368–375 in your textbook.

House of Burgesses	**Breed's Hill**	**Thomas Gage**
Concord	**Benedict Arnold**	**Bunker Hill**
Paul Revere	**John Pitcairn**	**Samuel Adams**
Patrick Henry	**Fort Ticonderoga**	**Lexington**

A. Groups of men led by _____ and Ethan Allen captured _____ without firing a shot.

B. _____, along with two other men, rode to warn John Hancock and _____ that British troops led by General _____ were coming to get them.

C. _____ made a fiery speech to the Virginia _____ in support of fighting against the British.

D. The battle of _____ was actually fought on _____, and it was won by the British, despite the death of British Major _____.

E. Colonial militia fought against the British in the towns of _____ and _____, signaling the beginning of the American Revolution.

Name _____ Date _____

Using Battle Maps

Look at the battle map below. Then answer the questions that follow.
For help with this skill, see pages 376–377 in your textbook.

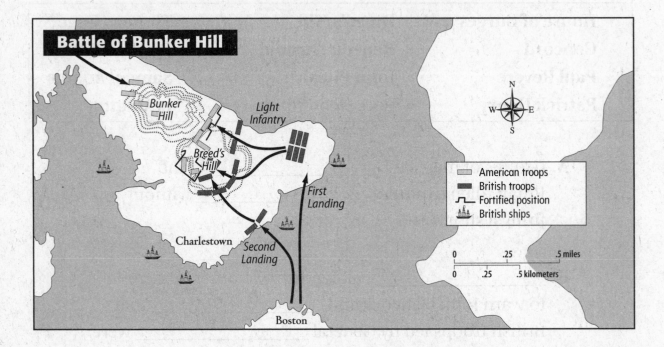

1. On what hill did the American troops build a fort? _____

2. British troops came from what city to capture the American fort? _____

3. Which troops were in the Northwest? _____

4. Which side had more soldiers? _____

Standard: 5.6.1   Chapter 11, Use Battle Maps

A Daring Declaration

Read this excerpt from the Declaration of Independence. Then answer the questions that follow. For help, see pages 378–383 in your textbook.

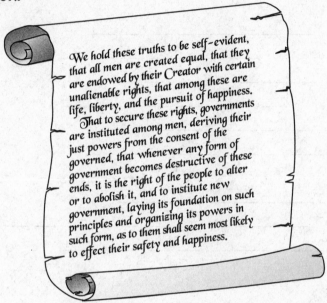

We hold these truths to be self-evident, that all men are created equal, that they are endowed by their Creator with certain unalienable rights, that among these are life, liberty, and the pursuit of happiness. That to secure these rights, governments are instituted among men, deriving their just powers from the consent of the governed, that whenever any form of government becomes destructive of these ends, it is the right of the people to alter or to abolish it, and to institute new government, laying its foundation on such principles and organizing its powers in such form, as to them shall seem most likely to effect their safety and happiness.

1. How did the pamphlet *Common Sense* by Thomas Paine influence colonists? _____
_____
_____

2. What two things were deleted from Jefferson's draft of the Declaration of Independence? Why? _____
_____
_____
_____

3. Why did it take courage to sign the Declaration of Independence?
_____

4. Why is the Declaration of Independence still important to people today? _____
_____
_____

War of Words

Solve each clue to fill in the blanks. Then use the boxed letters to answer the riddle below. For help, see pages 390–396 in your textbook.

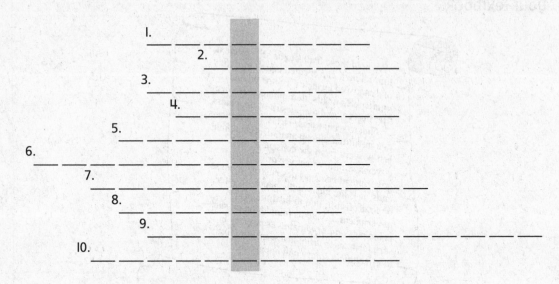

Clues

1. what people who supported the Revolution called themselves

2. nickname for a British soldier

3. what African Americans hoped would end as a result of the Declaration of Independence

4. a Native American group that fought on the British side

5. name for a colonist who supported the British and who did not want independence

6. a plan of government, written by each state

7. how some people got rich during the war by raising prices on goods

8. German soldiers hired by the British

9. a woman who dressed as a man in order to join the Continental army

10. foreign soldiers who were paid to fight

According to John Adams, what was "in the minds and hearts of the people"? _____

How Did We Win?

For each question, circle the letter of the correct answer. For help, see pages 400–407 in your textbook.

1. What did the battles at Princeton and Saratoga have in common?

    a. They were both important victories for the British.

    b. They were both fought at sea.

    c. They were both won in part by taking the enemy by surprise.

2. Which of the following factors did NOT contribute to the British defeat at Saratoga?

    a. The British leader was overconfident.

    b. The Americans had far more soldiers than the British.

    c. Hessian soldiers had brought their wives with them.

3. Why was the victory at Saratoga especially important?

    a. It won important lands from the Canadians.

    b. A top British general was killed.

    c. Other countries began to send aid to the Americans.

4. Why was the winter at Valley Forge particularly tough for the Continental army?

    a. The army was forced to train under a cruel instructor.

    b. Supplies promised by the government did not come.

    c. The British constantly attacked the camp.

5. Why do we use the name "Benedict Arnold" as a synonym for "traitor"?

    a. Arnold refused to participate in the fighting on either side.

    b. Arnold betrayed the Americans by selling information to the British.

    c. Arnold exposed Major John Andre as a traitor.

Name _____ Date _____

A Question of Scale

Look at the two maps drawn to different scales. Use them to answer the questions that follow. For help, see pages 408–409 in your textbook.

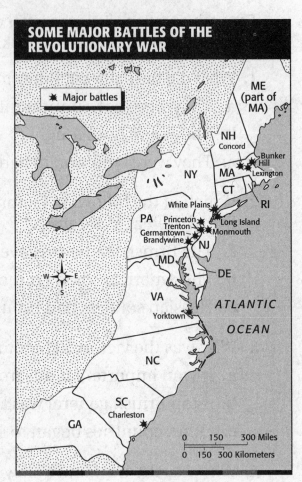

SOME MAJOR BATTLES OF THE REVOLUTIONARY WAR

TROOP MOVEMENTS IN NEW JERSEY AND PENNSYLVANIA

1. Which colonies are featured on the large-scale map?

   _____

2. Which battle locations are shown on the small-scale map but not the large-scale map?

   _____

3. What information can be learned from the large-scale map but not the small-scale map? _____

   _____

   _____

4. What towns are featured on the large-scale map and not the small-scale map? _____

   _____

Victory!

Use the words in the box to fill in the blanks in the Cause and
Effect chart. For help, see pages 414–418 in your textbook.

closed	peace	surrounded	support
Yorktown	South	slavery	ally
supplies	taxes	sided	
land	North	British	

Cause	Effect
Spain was an _____ of France.	Spain _____ its port at New Orleans to the British.
The British had been defeated in the _____ and the West.	The British then looked to the _____.
Congress had very little money and almost no _____ for the army.	Between 1778 and 1781 the _____ won several battles in the South.
Cornwallis hoped to let his army rest at _____.	American and French armies _____ Cornwallis.
The British people were tired of paying _____ for the war.	The British government agreed to start _____ talks.
After the war, the American government needed the _____ of Southern plantation owners.	Despite the hopes of African Americans, _____ continued.
Americans took _____ from Native Americans.	Native Americans _____ with the British during the war.

© Macmillan/McGraw-Hill

Create a Monument

Nations often honor ideas, people, or events by building monuments. In this activity you will be part of a group that is designing a monument honoring the ideas, people, or events of the American Revolution.

1. In your group, use your textbook to review the reasons for the American Revolution and the people who fought or supported it.

2. Collect ideas about different monuments.

3. Organize your group so that some students record information on the American Revolution while others research monuments.

4. After you have decided who or what to feature on your monument, design it. You may have to make many sketches before your group is satisfied with the design.

5. Your group will make several drawings of your monument, called architectural drawings. Each drawing will show the monument from a different view, such as the front or back. You may want to consider including a view from above.

6. On the back of each view, write an explanation of what that view shows.

7. Select a spokesperson from your group to present the design to the class. Make sure you can explain why your group selected the people or ideas featured, and why the monument's design is suited to the subject.

How Alike? How Different?

Read the paragraphs below. Then fill in the chart by comparing and contrasting the two competing plans for setting up our national government. For help with this skill, see pages 434–435 in your textbook.

Madison's Virginia Plan suggested an elected legislature split into two parts known as "houses." The members of the first house would be elected by citizens, but members of the second house would be chosen by members of the first house. The government would be based on the population of each state.

Roger Sherman suggested that the legislature be broken into two parts. In the House of Representatives, each state would be represented according to its population. However, in the Senate, each state, no matter what its size, would have two votes. Sherman's proposal, adopted on July 16, 1787, is known as the "Great Compromise."

Compare and Contrast Diagram

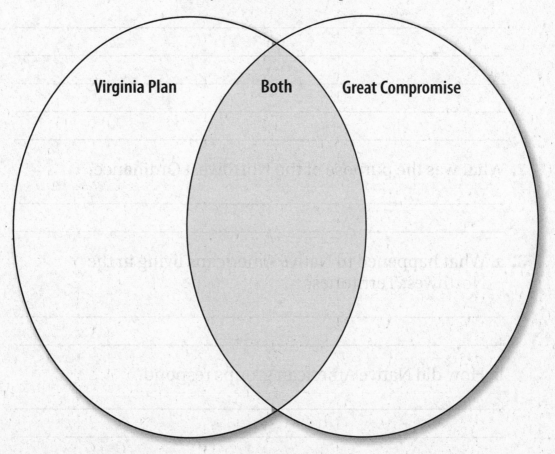

Virginia Plan   Both   Great Compromise

Life Under the Articles

Answer the questions that follow. For help, see pages 438–443 in your textbook.

1. This cartoon shows which weakness of the Articles of Confederation?

_____

_____

_____

_____

_____

2. What was the purpose of the Northwest Ordinance?

_____

_____

3. a. What happened to Native Americans living in the Northwest Territories?

_____

_____

b. How did Native American groups respond?

_____

_____

Standards: 5.6.6, 5.7.1   Chapter 13, Lesson 1

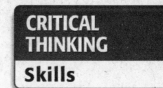
Identifying Bias

The speech below could have been made by a settler in the Northwest Territory. The words and phrases underlined in the speech show bias. Write them below with an explanation as to why they show bias. For help with this skill, see pages 444–445 in your textbook.

"It is not enough to defend ourselves against Indians when they come to invade our homes. Those <u>cowards</u> come in swift raids instead of fighting in the open like <u>civilized</u> men. By the time we see them coming, it may be too late! Who does not <u>shudder</u> to think of what would happen if the <u>savages</u> were able to get past our defenses? No. We must organize a party to take the fight to the Shawnee. Until we have completely eliminated the <u>mortal threat</u> they pose, we will never be able to convince settlers to come to the Northwest Territory and help us form a state."

_____   _____

_____   _____

_____   _____

_____   _____

_____   _____

_____   _____

_____   _____

_____   _____

_____   _____

A Constitutional Crossword

Solve the clues about the Constitutional Convention to complete the puzzle. For help, see pages 447–450 in your textbook.

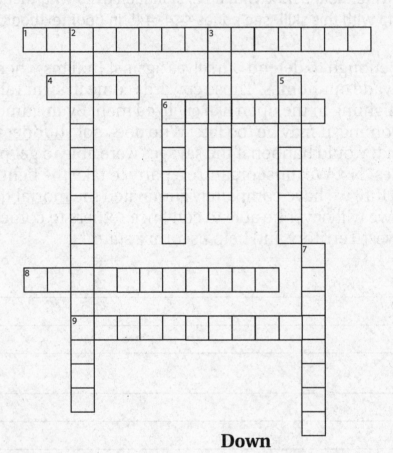

Across

1. the agreement that required both a Senate and a House of Representatives to approve a new law
4. refusing to approve a law is also called a _____.
6. the delegate who proposed the Great Compromise
8. the only state that did not send a delegate to the Constitutional Convention
9. a group of people elected to make laws

Down

2. to become President, a candidate must win the majority vote of this group
3. he proposed the New Jersey Plan
5. "Father of the Constitution"
6. the legislative body that gives two votes to each state
7. a person chosen to speak or act for others

© Macmillan/McGraw-Hill

Analyze the Data

Analyze the line graph and the circle graph. Then answer the questions below. For help with this skill, see pages 452–453 in your textbook.

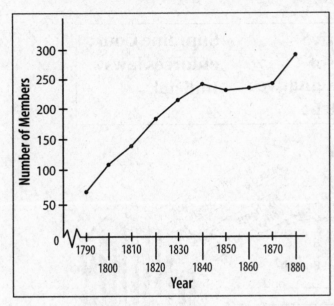

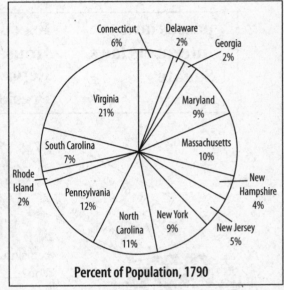

Percent of Population, 1790

1. On a circle graph, what percentage is the entire graph? _____

2. Describe the overall trend of the line graph.

   _____

   _____

3. What does the line graph tell you about the United States?

   _____

   _____

4. **a.** About what percent of the U.S. population was represented by the two senators from Rhode Island in 1790? _____

   b. According to these percentages, was Virginia or Rhode Island better represented in the Senate? Explain.

   _____

   _____

   _____

   _____

A Balancing Act

Use the words and phrases in the box to complete the chart. Then answer the questions that follow. For help, see pages 456–459 in your textbook.

passes laws interprets laws Senate	Executive House of Representatives President	Supreme Court enforces laws Judicial

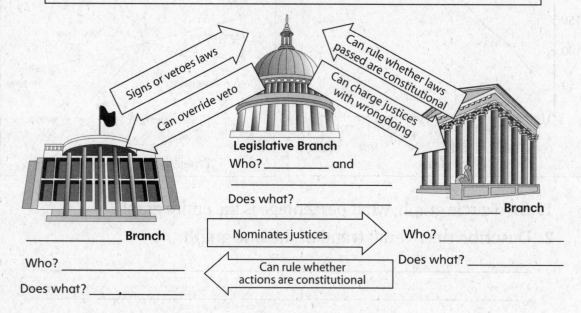

1. a. What is the system of checks and balances?

_____

_____

_____

b. Why is it important?

_____

_____

_____

2. The President of the United States has the right to veto a new law. How can Congress override that veto?

_____

_____

Constitution Evolution

Put your knowledge of the Constitution to the test by answering these questions. For help, see pages 458–463 in your textbook.

George Washington was a Federalist.

What was a Federalist?

_____

_____

_____

_____

_____

Patrick Henry was an Antifederalist.

Why did Antifederalists oppose the idea of a U.S. Constitution?

_____

_____

_____

_____

The Bill of Rights is a list of liberties to which all Americans are entitled.

Name three liberties guaranteed by the Bill of Rights:

_____

_____

_____

_____

Chapter 13, Lesson 4   Standards: 5.7.2, 5.7.3, 5.7.4   65

Name _____ Date _____

Building the New Republic

Write the letter from each portrait next to the two statements that describe each person's accomplishments. For help, see pages 467–469 in your textbook.

A. George Washington

B. Thomas Jefferson

C. Benjamin Banneker

1. _____ Co-founded one of the United States' first political parties, the Democratic-Republicans.

2. _____ Helped plan a new capital for the United States, called the District of Columbia.

3. _____ Served as the nation's first President, serving two consecutive terms.

4. _____ Was one of the first African Americans ever appointed by a President to work for the federal government.

5. _____ As the first Secretary of State, he handled affairs with other nations.

6. _____ As President, he established a system of calling department heads together for advice. It's known as the Cabinet.

Go West!

Read the statements carefully. Circle the correct answer for "True" or "False," or answer the questions. For help, see pages 475–478 in your textbook.

1. In 1790, 95 percent of Americans lived east of the Appalachians.

   True   False

2. Most of the people who moved west were wealthy Americans.

   True   False

3. About what fraction of the American population lived in poverty in 1820?

   _____

   _____

4. Most pioneer children had a formal education.

   True   False

5. What kept many pioneer children from attending school?

   _____

Match Game

Draw a line from each picture to that person's description.
For help, see pages 483-487 in your textbook.

1. Meriwether Lewis

2. John Marshall

3. Zebulon Pike

Explorer who tried to find the source of the Mississippi River

Interpreter and guide for the Lewis and Clark Expedition

Thomas Jefferson's personal secretary

Supreme Court justice who was impeached by the House of Representatives

Chief Justice who wrote the *Marbury versus Madison* decision

President who wanted to expand the United States to the west

4. Samuel Chase

5. Sacagawea

6. Thomas Jefferson

© Macmillan/McGraw-Hill

Mr. Madison's War

Answer the questions below. For help, see pages 490–495 in your textbook.

1. Which area of the United States refused to fight "Mr. Madison's War"? _____

2. What area did the United States acquire in the Adams-Onis Treaty of 1819? _____

3. Name some important victories for the American side in the War of 1812.

   _____

   _____

   _____

4. Make one generalization about the battles in the War of 1812.

   _____

   _____

   _____

5. Name the battle you think was most important in the War of 1812. Explain why you chose that battle.

   _____

   _____

   _____

   _____

   _____

Name _____ Date _____

Design Your Own Government

Join a small group in order to invent a new nation. Picture your group
as settlers on an isolated island.

1. Decide what your nation will be like and what kind of
   government you will create to protect the people and
   provide for their needs. To do this, use the questions below.
   Record your answers on a separate piece of paper. As you
   think of additional aspects of government you need to
   include, record this information, too.

   • Do you need a leader? If so, what will his or her job be,
     and how will he or she be chosen?

   • Do you need other people in the government? If so, what will
     their jobs be and how will they be chosen?

   • Who will make rules?

   • How will citizens' rights be protected?

   • What will be some of the island's most important rules?

2. Now that you have chosen your government, a new
   situation arises: A group of native islanders that you did
   not know about has appeared from the other side of the
   island. What course of action will you take towards this
   unknown group?

   _____

   _____

3. After designing your nation and government and dealing
   with a new situation, prepare a constitution for your island.

   • Make texts and charts that explain how the government
     works and what its laws are.

   • Present them to the class, explain why your group chose
     as it did, and tell how your settlement dealt with the
     native islanders and why.

Standards: 5.4.7, 5.5.1, 5.7.2, 5.7.3, 5.7.4　　Unit 5, Unit Activity

What Do You Conclude?

Read the paragraphs below. Copy the word web and fill it in by listing the main idea of the passage and four details. Use this information to draw a conclusion. For help with this skill, see pages 508–509 in your textbook.

In 1793 Southerners harvested about 180,000 pounds of cotton. By 1810 the harvest was 93 million pounds. This huge increase began with an inventor named Eli Whitney.

In 1792 Whitney visited a plantation in Georgia. He heard the farmer talking about the difficulty of removing cotton seeds by hand. Whitney built a cotton gin to remove seeds from cotton. Whitney's machine could clean 50 times more cotton in a few minutes than a whole team of workers could clean in a day.

With the cotton gin, plantation owners found that they could make huge profits by using more enslaved workers than ever before.

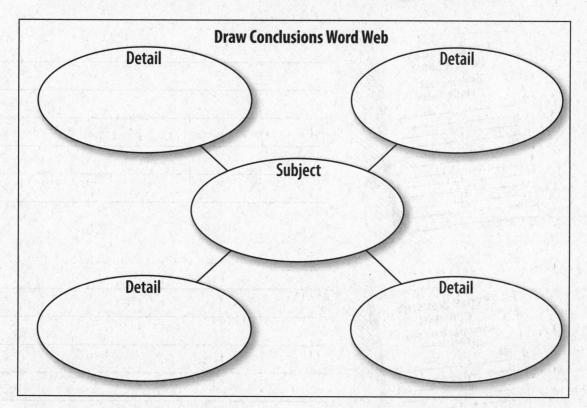

Draw Conclusions Word Web

Detail

Detail

Subject

Detail

Detail

Conclusion: _____

_____

_____

Industrial Revolution Gazette

The titles below could have appeared in American newspapers during the Industrial Revolution. Write two sentences that might have appeared in each article. For help, see pages 512–518 in your textbook.

KING COTTON TAKES THE WORLD BY STORM

COTTON HARVEST HITS RECORD SIZE

_____

_____

_____

_____

_____

_____

_____

LOWELL BUILDS POWER LOOM

REVOLUTIONIZES TEXTILE BUSINESS

_____

_____

_____

_____

_____

_____

_____

TEXTILE INDUSTRY BOOMING

NORTHENERS LEAVE FARMS FOR FACTORIES

_____

_____

_____

_____

_____

_____

_____

_____

Inspired Inventors

Think about the inventors and industrialists that you have read about. Try to determine what inspired them and what inventions they created as a result of their inspirations. Fill in the chart. Then use the information to make a generalization about these people. For help with this skill, see page 519 in your textbook.

Inventor or Industrialist	Got idea from…	Which resulted in…
Eli Whitney		
Samuel Slater		
Francis Cabot Lowell		

Generalization:

_____

_____

Full Steam Ahead!

Look at the timeline and the captions below. Under each date marked on the timeline, write the letter of the caption that goes with that date. Then answer the questions that follow. For help, see pages 521–523 in your textbook.

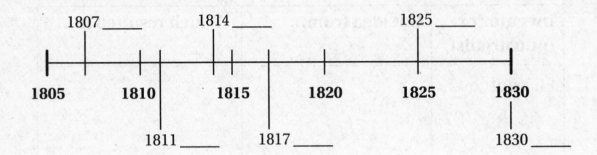

a. George Stephenson builds the first train with a steam engine.

b. Ships start traveling through a completed Erie Canal.

c. Robert Fulton's steamboat makes its first run up the Hudson River.

d. The National Road is built.

e. A small locomotive called *Tom Thumb* races a horse-drawn carriage.

f. Construction begins on the Erie Canal.

1. Why was it a challenge to build the Erie Canal?

_____

_____

_____

_____

_____

2. What effects did the Erie Canal have?

_____

_____

_____

_____

Standard: 5.8.1   Chapter 15, Lesson 2

Population Distribution Maps

Look at the population distribution map below. Then answer the
questions that follow. For help, see pages 524–525 in your textbook.

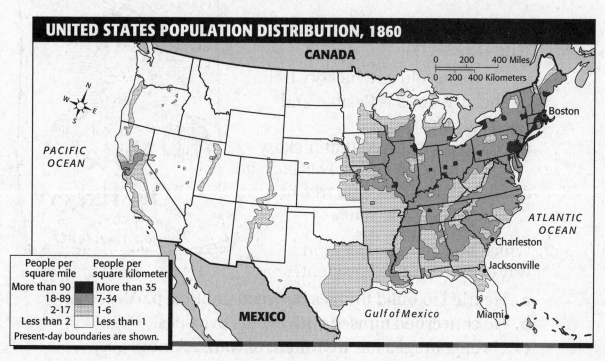

UNITED STATES POPULATION DISTRIBUTION, 1860

1. Describe the general distribution of population in the
   United States in 1860. _____

   _____

2. **a.** What was the population density of the Charleston area?

   _____

   b. What was the population density of the Boston area?

   _____

3. How many people per square mile lived in Jacksonville?

   _____

4. Which city had the fewest people per square mile?
   How many? _____

Name _____ Date _____

Old Hickory's History

Circle the letter of the correct answer to each question. For help, see pages 527–531 in your textbook.

1. Why was Andrew Jackson called "Old Hickory"?

   a. He was as old as a hickory tree.

   b. Hickory wood is flexible and so was Jackson.

   c. A soldier observed that hickory wood is tough and so was Jackson.

   d. Hickory was the state tree of Jackson's home state.

2. Which best describes Jackson's way of governing as President?

   a. He tried to build bridges between political parties.

   b. He concerned himself with events overseas.

   c. He encouraged fair treatment of Native Americans.

   d. He increased the power of the office of President.

3. Why did Jackson dislike the Bank of the United States?

   a. He believed it was unconstitutional.

   b. He believed the bank was stealing money.

   c. He believed it would make bad investment choices and lose money.

   d. He believed it favored farmers instead of wealthy people.

4. What did Jackson hope to accomplish with the Indian Removal Act?

   a. He hoped to end conflict between settlers and Native Americans for good.

   b. He hoped the Native Americans would settle Oklahoma and make it a new state.

   c. He hoped the different Native American groups would fight among themselves.

   d. He hoped Native Americans would be allowed to remove gold from Georgia.

Standard: 5.8.1   Chapter 15, Lesson 3

Changes Across the U.S.

Use the clues to complete the crossword puzzle. For help,
see pages 537–539.

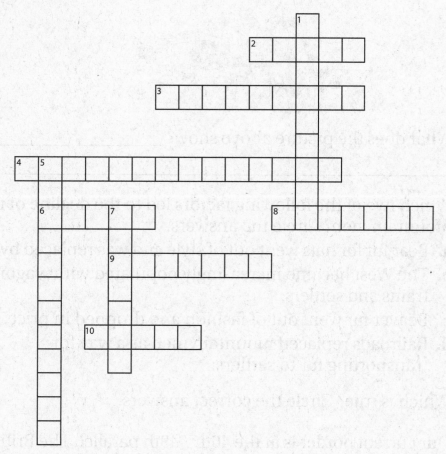

Across

2. places where immigrants
   entered the nation by ship

3. an energy source that replaced
   whale oil starting in the 1860s

4. a religious revival known as the
   Second _____ _____

6. a nation that was an important
   trade partner of the United
   States in the 1800s

8. fast, beautiful sailing ship that
   was replaced by the steamboat

9. an important industry in New
   England until it declined in
   the 1860s

10. the people who left their
    homeland to escape starvation,
    beginning in 1846

Down

1. the manmade waterway that
   connected Lake Erie and the
   Hudson River

5. the first black Methodist
   Episcopal minister in the
   United States

7. the largest city in the United
   States after 1825

Name _____ Date _____

On the Trail

Answer the questions and follow the instructions below. For help, see pages 548–553 in your textbook.

1. What does the picture above show? _____

_____

2. Which two of the following factors led to the decline of the mountain men? Circle the answers.
   a. Bear fur for hats went out of style and was replaced by silk.
   b. The West became increasingly populated with wagon trains and settlers.
   c. Beaver fur went out of fashion and dropped in price.
   d. Railroads replaced mountain men as a way for transporting fur to settlers.

3. Which is true? Circle the correct answers.

   Our current border is at the 40th / 49th parallel. The British / French agreed with President Polk to extend the border along that line all the way to the Atlantic / Pacific in 1846.

4. Circle the events, items, or people that do not fit into the time line covered in this lesson.

   a. Manifest Destiny   e. Oregon Trail

   b. Civil War   f. Women gain right
                                 to vote

   c. Mormons settle Utah   g. President Polk

   d. Mountain men   h. Signing of the
                                 Declaration of
                                 Independence

© Macmillan/McGraw-Hill

Where Do We Live Now?

Look at the cartogram below. Answer the questions that follow.
For help with this skill, see pages 554–555 in your textbook.

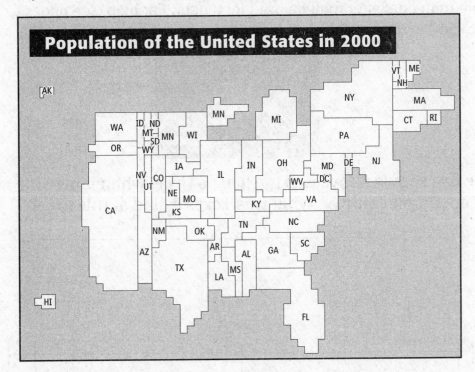

Population of the United States in 2000

1. Which state has the greatest population? _____

2. Compare the cartogram to a standard U.S. map. Name some states that are much smaller on the cartogram than they are on the standard map.

_____

_____

3. Rank these states in order of population size from smallest to largest: Michigan, Vermont, Texas, Washington.

1. _____

2. _____

3. _____

4. _____

Name _____ Date _____

Texas in Time

Answer the question. Then fill in the time line by placing the letter of the fact or event in the box that connects to the correct year. More than one letter may be used for a year. For help, see pages 556–560 in your textbook.

The flag shown above was the flag of Texas when it became an independent country. What was Texas called at this time?

_____

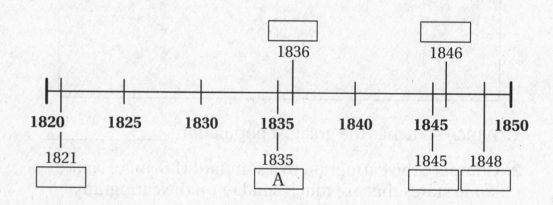

Fact or Event

A. 25,000 Americans live in Texas

B. Mexico wins independence from Spain

C. Texas votes to join the United States

D. fighting breaks out between American and Mexican troops

E. Congress votes to allow Texas into the Union

F. Moses Austin receives land in Mexico

G. The Treaty of Guadalupe Hidalgo is signed

H. Texas declares its independence from Mexico

I. The Bear Flag Republic is formed

What's the Source?

Answer the questions. Then do the activity that follows. You will need Internet access. For help with this skill, see page 561 in your textbook.

1. Suppose you had to write a report on the history of Texas. What types of organizations would produce the most reliable Web sites for your research?

_____

2. What keyword or words would you use to get information for your report? _____

3. Type your keyword into a search engine. Look at the results. Choose two Web sites, one from a source you think will be reliable and one you think may be less reliable. Complete the following chart.

Answers will vary because students' sources will vary.

	Reliable Source	Unreliable Source
What is the Web site's URL?		
Who publishes the Web site?		
Does the Web site have a stated goal? What is it?		
Do you see any bias or incorrect information? Explain.		
Do you believe this Web site is a reliable source? Why?		

Name _____ Date _____

Reporter's Notebook

Suppose you are a reporter interviewing the people listed below. What would each person say about life in California? Write each person's comments in your Reporter's Notebook. For help, see pages 562–567 in your textbook.

Forty-Niners Speak Out

A wealthy Californio: _____

_____

_____

A young woman working in a boardinghouse: _____

_____

_____

The owner of a mining supply store: _____

_____

_____

_____

A traveler to California with Gold Fever: _____

_____

_____

A Chinese miner: _____

_____

_____

Technology in the Spotlight

Working in groups, choose one new technology that was discussed in Unit 6. Using the information in the unit, create a skit on how your technology...

- was created, and why it was created

- influenced the time period in which it was invented

- has led to further developments in technology up to this day

- still influences us today

- might influence the future

1. Cover all topics in your skit and decide how to present issues about the past, present, and future.

2. Assign roles to each person so that everyone in the group becomes an expert in one aspect of the technology. Make sure your skit explains your group's ideas and information to the rest of the class.

3. Perform your skit for the class. Be prepared to answer questions from the class.

Name _____ Date _____

Read Between the Lines

Read the paragraphs below. Then copy the chart and fill it in. List details from the paragraphs in the first column. Make inferences based on those details in the second column. For help with this skill, see pages 584–585 in your textbook.

Whites in both the North and the South were among the growing numbers of abolitionists, or people who wanted to outlaw slavery. Angelina and Sarah Grimké, for example, were sisters from a slaveholding family in South Carolina. They were among the first women to speak publicly for abolition.

Those that escaped slavery were also active in the abolition movement. In 1842 Frederick Douglass stood before a large crowd of abolitionists. Douglass told the crowd that he stood before them as a thief who "stole this head, these limbs, this body from my master, and ran off with them." Sojourner Truth had also been enslaved and had escaped. Truth gave speeches around the country about abolition and women's rights.

Make Inferences Chart

Details	Inferences

Standards: 5.4.6, R2.4   Unit 7, Make Inferences

Politics and People

For each description on the left, fill in the correct letter of the person or phrase on the right. For help, see pages 588-593 in your textbook.

Sojourner Truth

Harriet Tubman

Sara and Angelina Grimké

1. founded a newspaper dedicated to ending slavery _____

2. when California entered the Union as a free state _____

3. editor of an antislavery newspaper, adviser to President Lincoln _____

4. said enslaved people are property without rights or privileges _____

5. passed in 1820; allowed slavery south of the 36th parallel _____

6. led people to freedom on the Underground Railroad _____

7. women who spoke publicly against slavery _____

8. law that required runaway enslaved Africans to be returned to their owners _____

9. escaped slave who supported abolition and women's rights _____

10. said Nebraska and Kansas can decide for themselves whether or not to allow slavery _____

a. Frederick Douglass

b. William Lloyd Garrison

c. Missouri Compromise

d. Compromise of 1850

e. Harriet Tubman

f. Sojourner Truth

g. Fugitive Slave Law

h. Kansas-Nebraska Act

i. Angelina and Sarah Grimké

j. Dred Scott Decision

Name _____ Date _____

Where Is It?

Use the organizational features of your textbook to answer the following questions. For help with this skill, see page 595 in your textbook.

1. Suppose you wanted to know where all of the biography pages were. Where could you look?

   _____

2. Use an organizational feature to find out what page Frederick Douglass's biography is on. What page is it? _____

3. You want to find all the pages on which Frederick Douglass is mentioned. Where should you look? _____

4. You are unsure of the meaning of a word you read in one of Douglass's speeches. Where should you look to find out what it means? _____

5. Where should you look to find the title of the next chapter and the lessons it contains?

   _____

6. What is the title of Chapter 18?

   _____

Chapter 17, Use Organizational Features of Texts

Mapping the War

Mark the map as directed. Then answer the questions that follow.
For help, see pages 596–599 in your textbook.

1. Color in green the states in the Confederacy.

2. Mark with an X the first state to secede from the Union.

3. Draw a circle on the state where the first major battle of the Civil War took place.

4. Color in red the state where Lincoln gave his Gettysburg Address.

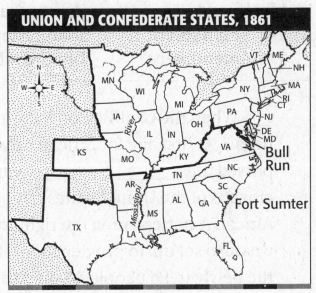

UNION AND CONFEDERATE STATES, 1861

5. What advantages did the Union have while fighting the Civil War? _____

_____

6. Why did Southern states secede from the Union?

_____

_____

_____

7. How did African Americans participate in the Civil War?

_____

_____

_____

_____

Name _____ Date _____

Paragraph Reconstruction

Use the words and phrases in the box to complete the sentences correctly. For help, see pages 602–605 in your textbook.

black codes	**Reconstruction**	**Freedman's Bureau**
14th Amendment	**sharecropping**	**segregation**
15th Amendment	**Jim Crow laws**	

When the Civil War ended, the era of _____ began. At first, life for African Americans improved. Congress passed the _____, which made African Americans citizens of the United States. The _____ gave African American men the right to vote. The _____ was also set up, to provide food, shelter, and other assistance to the newly freed people. Many African Americans became public officials in formerly slave-holding states.

Life quickly turned difficult once again for former slaves. Almost immediately, many southern states passed the _____. These state laws prevented African Americans from voting. Later, the _____ were passed to make _____, or separation based on race, legal. Because former slaves did not own land, many supported themselves with _____, which prevented them from getting ahead economically. For many African Americans, the coming decades would be a struggle.

Chapter 17, Lesson 3

Immigrants and Americans

Write a caption for each picture that describes that person's accomplishments. Then answer the questions. For help, see pages 611–614 in your textbook.

Mary Harris Jones

Samuel Gompers

_____   _____
_____   _____
_____   _____
_____   _____

1. a. Where did most immigrants to the United States come from during the 1870s–1920s? _____
_____

b. What did most immigrants do for work?
_____

c. In what kind of communities did most immigrants settle? _____

2. List three other areas of the world that immigrants left in order to come to the United States.

_____
_____
_____

3. What is the purpose of a labor union, and how does it work?

_____
_____

Name _____ Date _____

What Time Is It?

Use the time zone map below to answer the questions. For help with this skill, see pages 616-617 in your textbook.

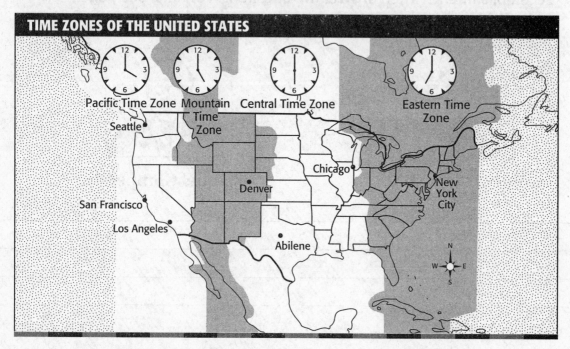

TIME ZONES OF THE UNITED STATES

1. **a.** How many time zones are there within the continental United States? _____

   b. What are they called? _____
   _____

2. What time zone is Chicago in? _____

3. If you were in Denver and someone called you from New York City, what time zone would the call be coming from?
   _____

4. What time zone is Denver in? _____

5. If it was 5 P.M. for the person calling you from New York City, what time would it be for you in Denver? _____

6. As you move from east to west, do you add or subtract an hour for each time zone you cross? _____

7. When it is 5 P.M. in Abilene, it is _____ in Seattle.

8. When it is 8 A.M. in San Francisco, what time is it in New York City? _____

Chapter 18, Use Time Zone Maps

Life in the Big City

Complete the following statements about American life around 1900. For help, see pages 619–622 in your textbook.

1. Jacob Riis wrote a book about life in city slums. It's called _____.

2. When great numbers of African Americans moved to northern cities, this was called the _____.

3. Immigrants often formed societies when they arrived in America. Mexicans called their groups _____.

4. When people are treated unfairly because of skin color, religion, gender, language, culture, or the country they come from, it's called _____.

5. In 1889, _____ founded a community center called a settlement house to provide services for immigrants.

6. The Nineteenth Amendment was passed in 1920. It gave women the _____.

Name _____ Date _____

One Man's Point of View

In the 1800s and early 1900s, many people saw the crowded city slums as a place where poverty, crime, and ignorance were allowed to grow. Read Jacob Riis's ideas about how to solve this problem. Then answer the questions. For help with this skill, see pages 624-625 in your textbook.

"[T]he rescue of the children is the key to the problem of city poverty.... [so] that character may be formed where to reform it would be a hopeless task.... [T]he young are naturally neither vicious nor hardened, simply weak and undeveloped, except by the bad influences of the street, [which] makes this duty all the more urgent as well as hopeful."

—from *How the Other Half Lives* by Jacob Riis, 1890

1. What is Jacob Riis's point of view in this paragraph?

_____

_____

2. What are some value words that the writer uses to express his point of view? _____

_____

3. What is his opinion about poor children?

_____

_____

4. Do you agree with the writer's point of view? Why or why not? _____

_____

_____

Immigration Over Time

Write one fact about immigration that relates to each of the numbered events on the time line. For help, see pages 627–628 in your textbook.

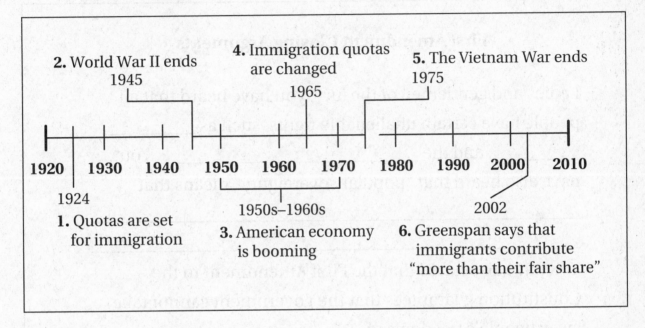

2. World War II ends
1945

4. Immigration quotas are changed
1965

5. The Vietnam War ends
1975

1920 1930 1940 1950 1960 1970 1980 1990 2000 2010

1924

1. Quotas are set for immigration

1950s–1960s

3. American economy is booming

2002

6. Greenspan says that immigrants contribute "more than their fair share"

1. _____
   _____

2. _____

3. _____
   _____

4. _____
   _____
   _____

5. _____
   _____

6. _____
   _____

Know Your Rights

You are a lawyer writing a closing argument for a court case defending the First Amendment. Fill in the spaces to complete the closing argument. For help, see pages 636–639 in your textbook.

First Amendment Closing Arguments

Ladies and gentlemen of the jury, you have heard that all people have certain unalienable rights, such as _____, _____, and the _____. You have also heard that "popular sovereignty" means that _____ _____.

You have also heard that the First Amendment to the Constitution guarantees that the government cannot take away people's freedoms of _____, _____, _____, _____, and _____. This is especially important in the United States because _____ _____ _____. Please consider this while you decide the fate of the First Amendment.

Thank you.

Standards: 5.7.3, 5.7.4, 5.7.5   Chapter 19, Lesson 1

To Believe or Not to Believe

Use the Internet to research the First Amendment. Find one source you believe is credible. Use the information from it to answer the following questions. For help, see pages 640–641 in your textbook.

1. What is the Web site address?

_____

2. What is the name of the Web site?

_____

3. Who publishes it (individual or organization)?

_____

_____

4. What qualifications does the author have?

_____

_____

5. What is the author's point of view?

_____

_____

6. What sources does the author list, if any?

_____

_____

_____

7. Explain why you believe this Web site is or is not a credible source.

_____

_____

_____

A Gallery of Leaders

Write a caption to describe each of the people shown below. Then answer the questions that follow. For help, see pages 642–647 in your textbook.

Martin Luther King Jr.

Rosa Parks

Thurgood Marshall

_____   _____   _____

_____   _____   _____

_____   _____   _____

_____   _____   _____

_____   _____   _____

_____   _____   _____

_____   _____   _____

1. What did the 1964 Civil Rights Act do? _____

_____

_____

_____

2. What do Sandra Day O'Connor and Condoleezza Rice have in common? _____

_____

_____

3. What other groups were inspired by the progress African Americans were able to make during the Civil Rights Movement? _____

_____

Standards: 5.7.3, 5.7.4, 5.7.5   Chapter 19, Lesson 2

A Challenging Time

For each question, circle the letter of the correct answer. For help, see pages 650–653 in your textbook.

1. What is one negative impact on the United States of the increase in global trade?

    a. Jobs are moving to poorer countries.

    b. Goods move around more easily than they have in the past.

    c. Consumer prices are lower.

    d. Competition among companies is increased.

2. Which best describes what the NAFTA agreement says?

    a. A set number of U.S. jobs will move to Mexico each year.

    b. Canada, Mexico, and the U.S. trade freely with each other.

    c. Canada, Mexico, and the U.S. trade only with each other.

    d. Canada, Mexico, and the U.S. are now one nation.

3. What causes global warming?

    a. melting glaciers

    b. greenhouse gases

    c. using less electricity

    d. acid rain

4. Which of the following statements about terrorists is true?

    a. Terrorists always attack countries besides their own.

    b. Terrorists do not have any goals besides making people afraid.

    c. There have never been any American-born terrorists.

    d. Terrorists use fear and violence to accomplish their goals.

5. Which of the following is NOT an example of participating in our democracy?

    a. registering other people to vote

    b. improving life in the community

    c. helping someone run for a national office

    d. All are examples of participating in democracy.

Reach Out and Ask

In this activity, you will write a letter to someone who works to protect our liberties.

1. Work in pairs to discuss the different jobs that protect our liberties. Examples of this could be the President, military personnel, police officers, elected officials, political activists, or newspaper reporters.

2. Choose one of the jobs. Working together, come up with five questions to ask a person with the job you chose.

3. Write a letter to someone in this position. In the letter, introduce yourselves, explain the project you are working on, and ask your questions. Your teacher will help you address the letter to the proper person when you are finished.

4. Discuss the response you get from your letter, and make notes about the person's role in protecting our liberties.

5. Share what you have learned with the class.

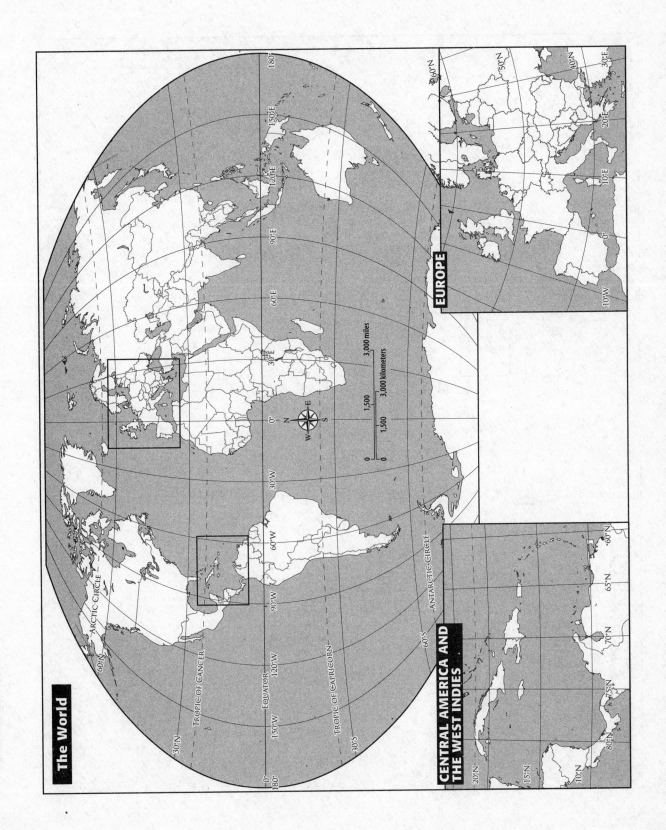

The World

EUROPE

CENTRAL AMERICA AND
THE WEST INDIES

© Macmillan/McGraw-Hill

The United States: Political

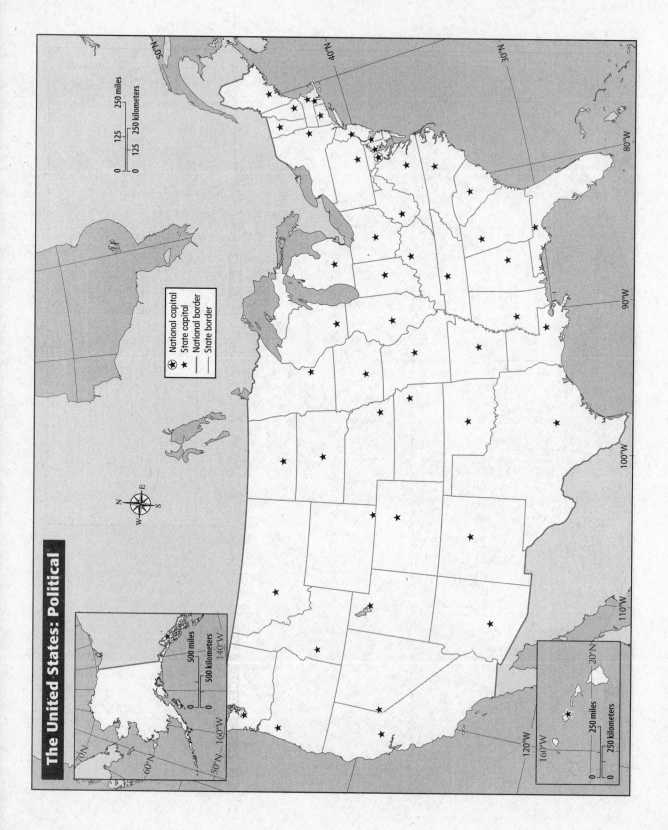

National capital
State capital
National border
State border

250 miles
250 kilometers

500 miles
500 kilometers

250 miles
250 kilometers

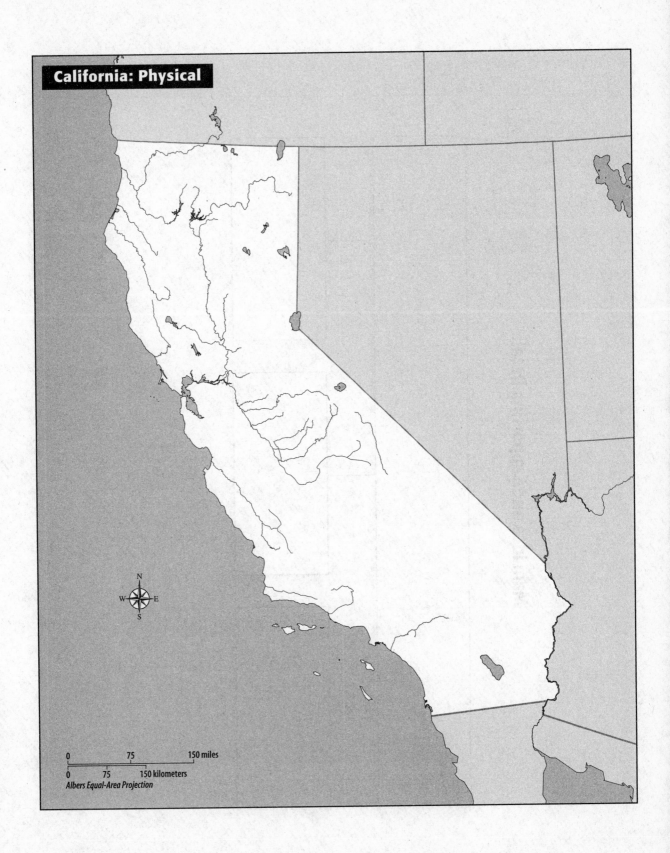

California: Physical

0 — 75 — 150 miles
0 — 75 — 150 kilometers
Albers Equal-Area Projection

Main Idea and Supporting Details

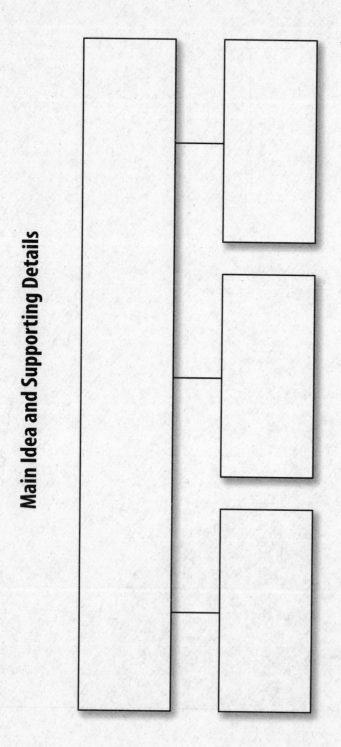

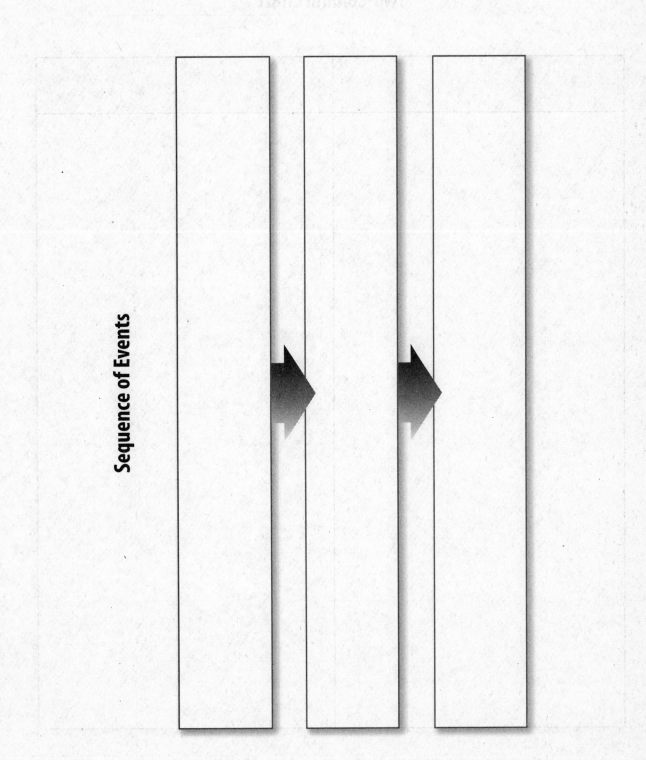

Sequence of Events

Two-Column Chart

Cause and Effect Table

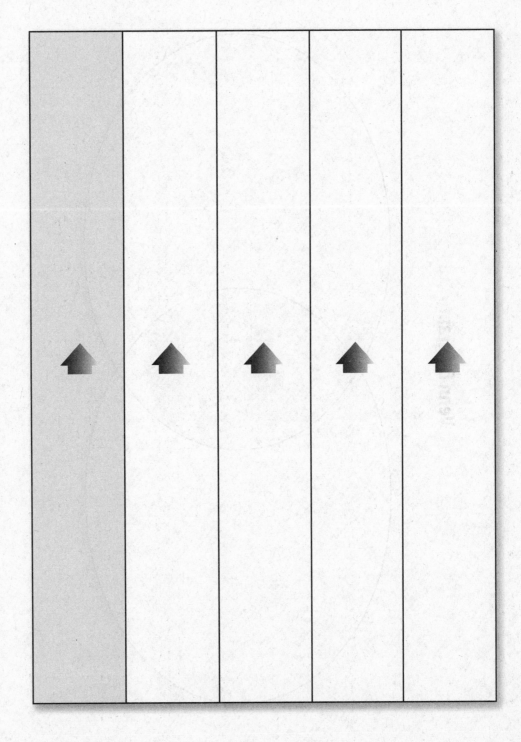

Venn Diagram

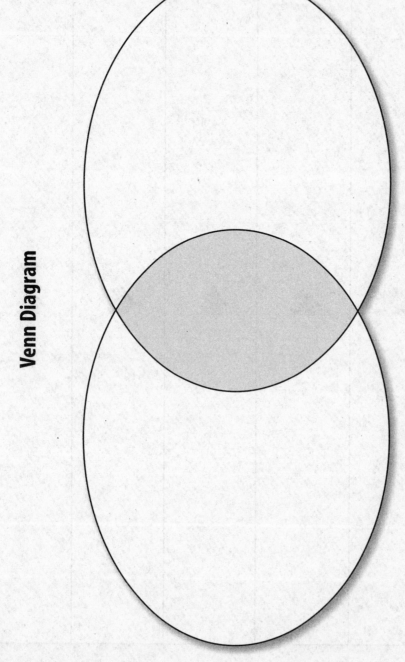

Word Web